EXTREME DOT-TO-DOT

The Day of the Dead

Dot to dot artworks by Patricia Moffett

CARLTON
BOOKS

W elcome to *Extreme Colouring: Day of the Dead* and the challenge waiting for you! To reveal each image, you'll join together 1001 numbered dots in order, and when you're finished connecting the dots, you can use colouring tools – pens, pencils, crayons, highlighters – to bring the image to life.

As you complete each puzzle, you'll learn about a festival that has its origins in a world of human sacrifice. That culture is now long gone, but the goddess of the dead was not forgotten, and she evolved through the years. By the beginning of the twentieth century, she had become an icon of protest, and a revolution followed.

Today the Day of the Dead is a celebration that unites a country, and it is travelling across the world. Perhaps that's because it makes remembering the dead a joyful experience, a time for sharing memories and laughing, rather than a grim experience as it is viewed in many other cultures.

Where the dots are clustered, we've sometimes used darker colours for the dots and their corresponding number to help you out. If you need further assistance, all the solutions are printed at the back of the book.

The Day of the Dead is a festival that's been hundreds of years in the making, and the word that describes it best is "exuberance." An altar strewn with Aztec marigolds is a dazzle of oranges and golds. Catrina, the Lady of the Dead, parades in finery that's taken months to prepare.

The artists who create *calaveras* (sugar skulls) compete for awards. It's colour, colour, colour by day and night. And that's what your puzzles will need after the dots are connected: colour. Joining the dots to reveal the image is just the start!

1.

The Day of the Dead is a tradition that has its roots in the culture of the Aztecs, warrior people who dominated Mexico and Central America until the arrival of the Spanish *conquistadores* in the sixteenth century.

2.

Their dead journeyed, so the Aztecs believed, to Mictlan, an underworld located to the north. Its queen was Mictecacihuatl, who was born in the days before the first humans, when the world was still young.

3.

While still an infant, Mictecacihuatl was sacrificed to the underworld. Deprived of life, she continued to grow, and is now an elegant skeleton with considerable powers. Her role is to watch over the bones of the dead.

4.

Mictecacihuatl once failed in this role, and Xolotl, the god of sickness and lightning, stole a corpse. From this, modern human beings were created. If a human corpse is ever stolen, the gods will create a new and terrible race.

5.

Mictecacihuatl loves flowers, and the Aztec marigold –
or *flor de muertos* – is sacred to her. The scent of their
blooms can wake the souls of the dead and bring them
back each year to the land of the living.

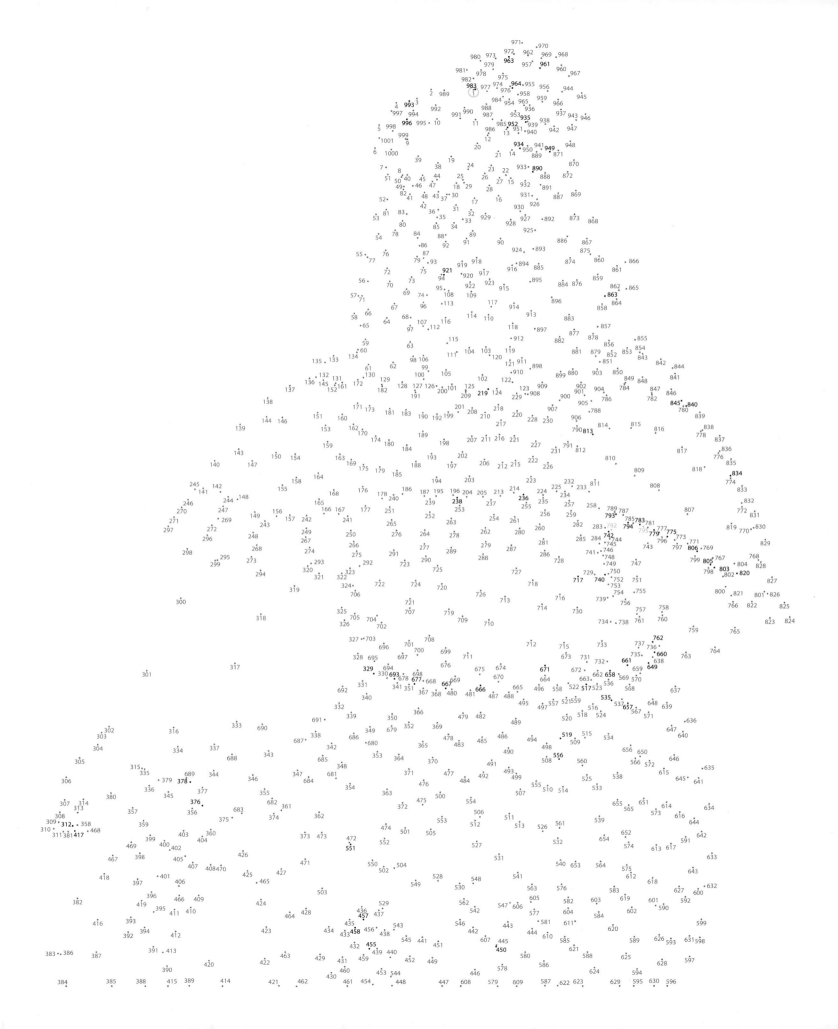

6.

Then, as now, altars were festooned with the marigolds –
a flower that grows wild across Central America. Petals are
sometimes strewn from the front door to the altar, leading
the souls to the heart of the family home.

7.

The altar has three levels, said to represent Heaven, Earth and Purgatory – which reveals the influence of the Catholic Church. In the underworld of the Aztecs, there were nine levels, and the journey through them all was hard.

8.

The Aztecs dominated the region for centuries. The Spanish conquered them in less than three years. They brought with them their Catholic traditions, including All Saints' Eve, All Saints' Day and All Souls' Day. The latter commemorates all who have died, especially family members.

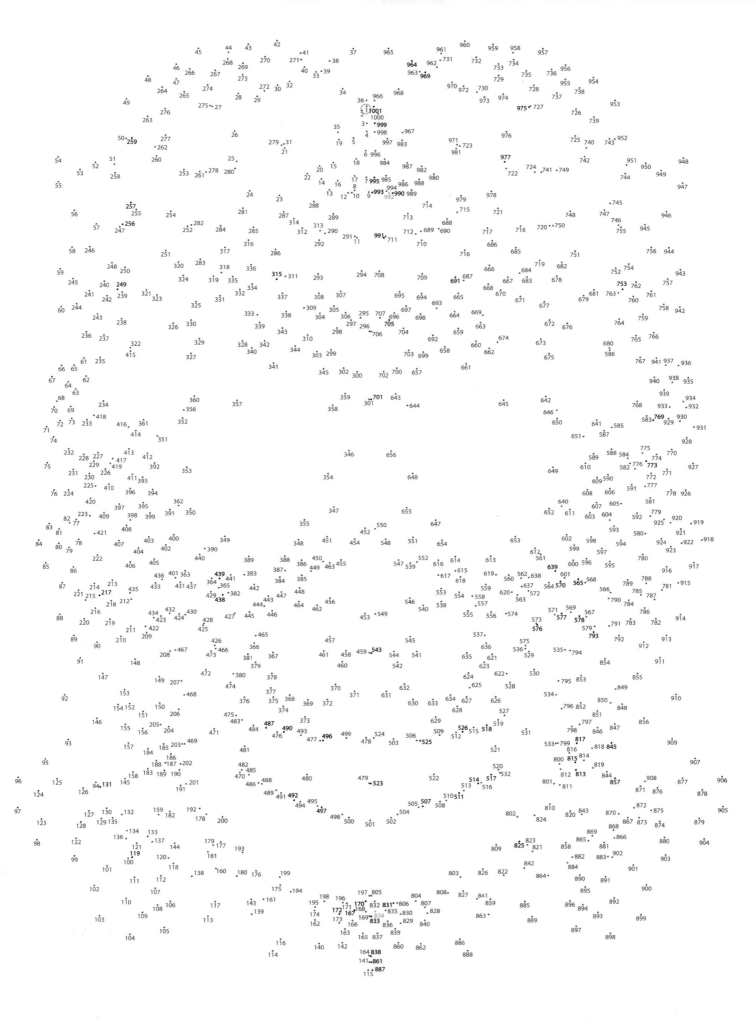

9.

Sharing a similar purpose, the Aztec and Christian festivals gradually became intertwined, and today the Day of the Dead is 2 November. The Aztec traditions continue, though, each family coming together to build an altar at home.

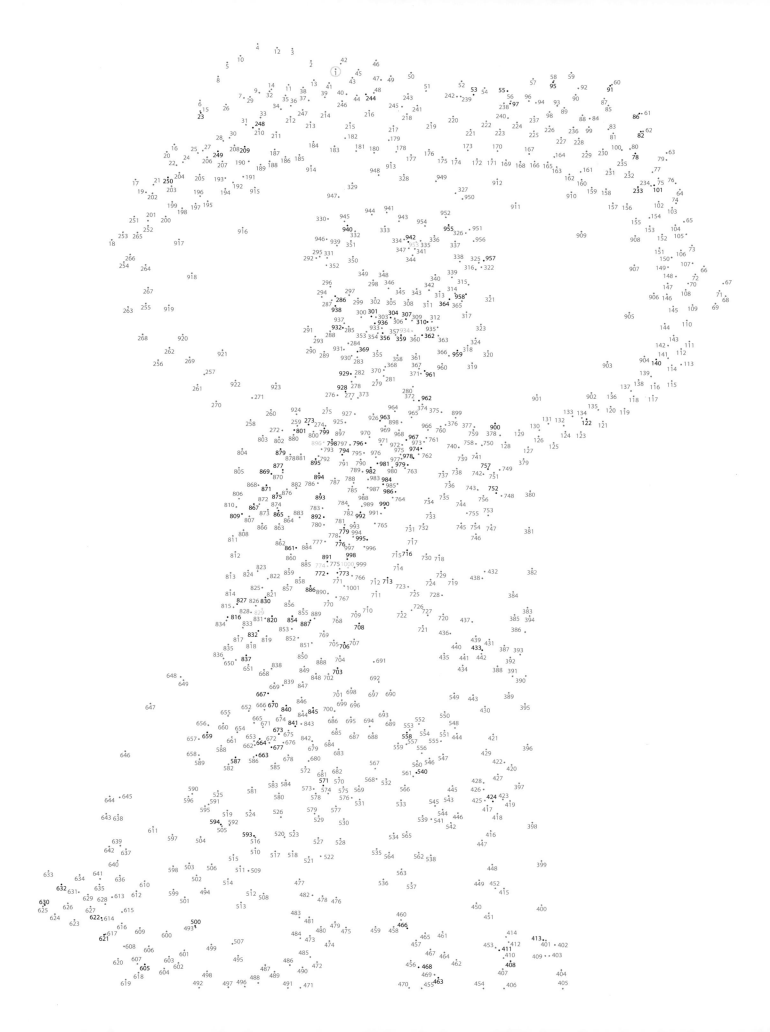

10.

Across Mexico, the rituals and their meaning change
from region to region. In Michoacán, for example, the
festival coincides with the migration of the monarch
butterflies, returning from the north. They are
believed to be the returning souls.

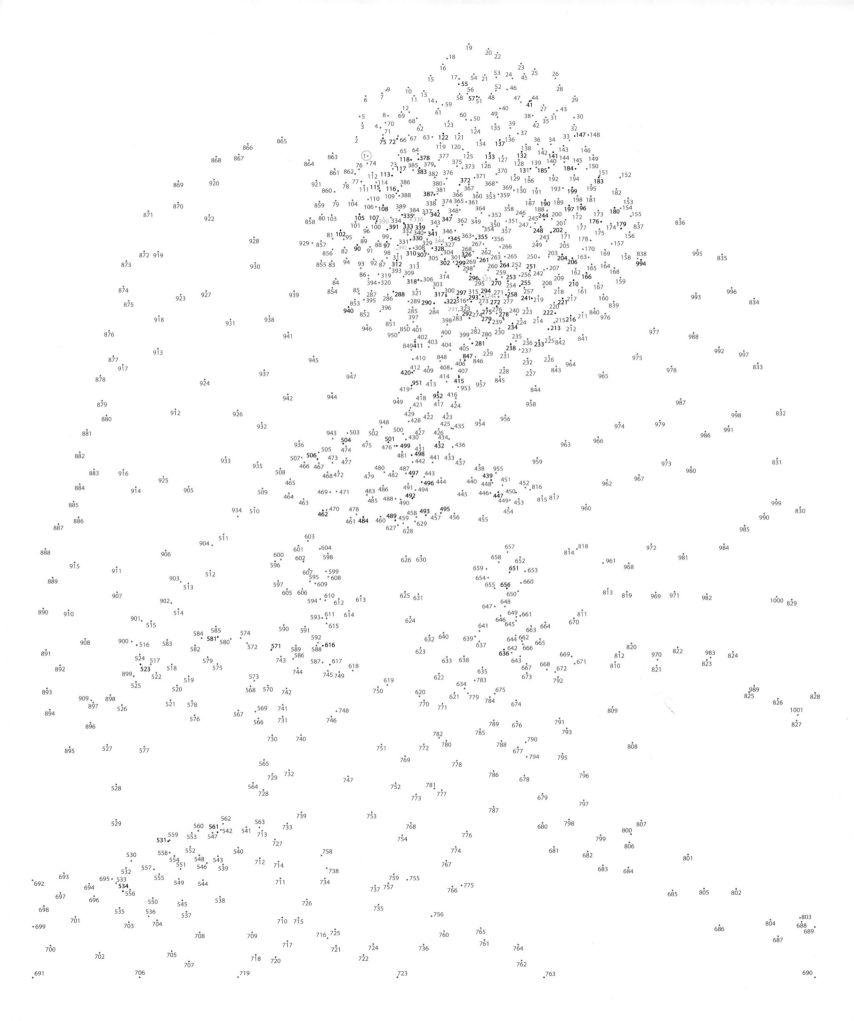

11.

What is constant throughout Mexico is the importance of the day – families may spend more than two months' income to celebrate their dead relatives. The expense is justified: souls who are happy protect the living and bring good luck.

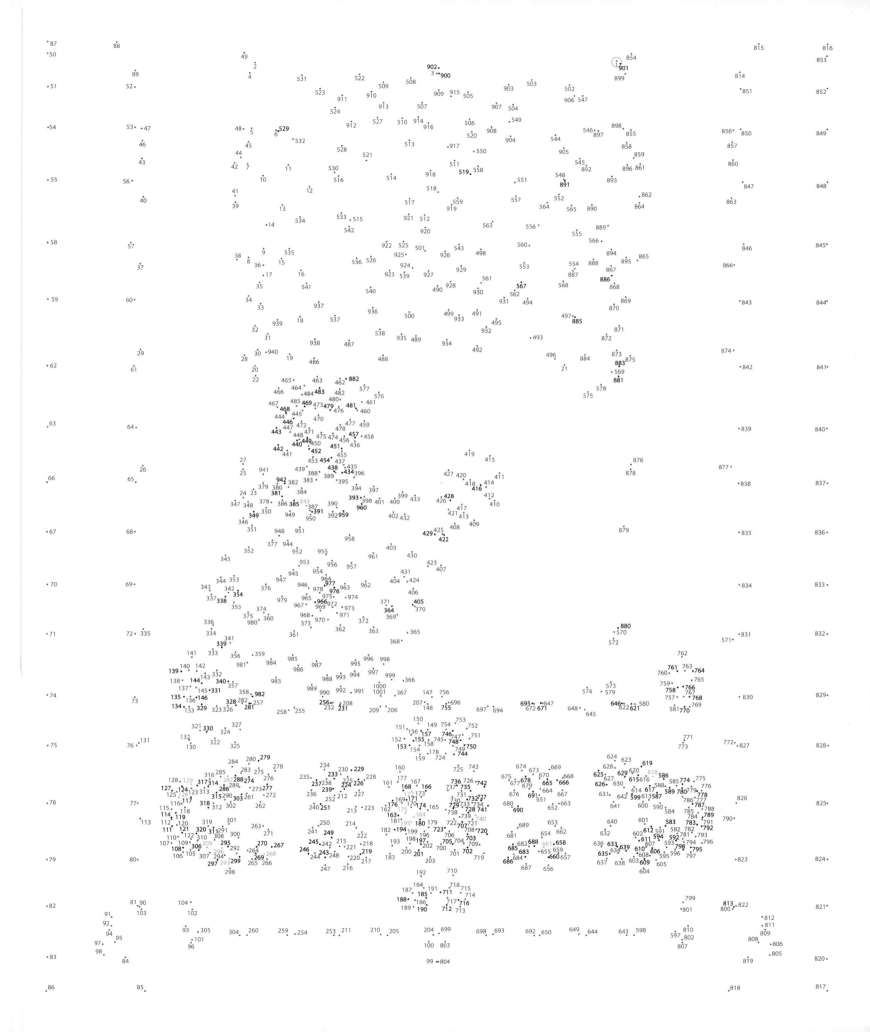

12.
Souls who have been overlooked may seek vengeance,
particularly if they compare notes with other spirits
whose families have been generous. It is said that those
who ignore their dead relatives will soon fall ill –
and they may even die.

13.
The whole family comes together to prepare the altar, and inevitably talk about who has died. Stories are remembered, jokes are told, and for children this is an opportunity to talk about dying without getting upset.

14.

Along with photographs, treats are laid out for the dead –
a shot of tequila perhaps or, for a child, a favourite toy.
The dead may want to refresh themselves after their long
journey, so a mirror and a washbasin are essential.

15.

The dead may also be hungry and thirsty, so lots of water and food will be on offer. *Pan de muerto*, or "dead man's bread", is a soft bread (like brioche) that is sometimes iced white, the colour of bones.

16.

There is a theory that *pan de muerto* reveals the influence of the Spanish. They introduced wheat to the Americas, and were appalled by the human sacrifices. A sweet bread, sometimes shaped into a human figure, seemed like a good compromise.

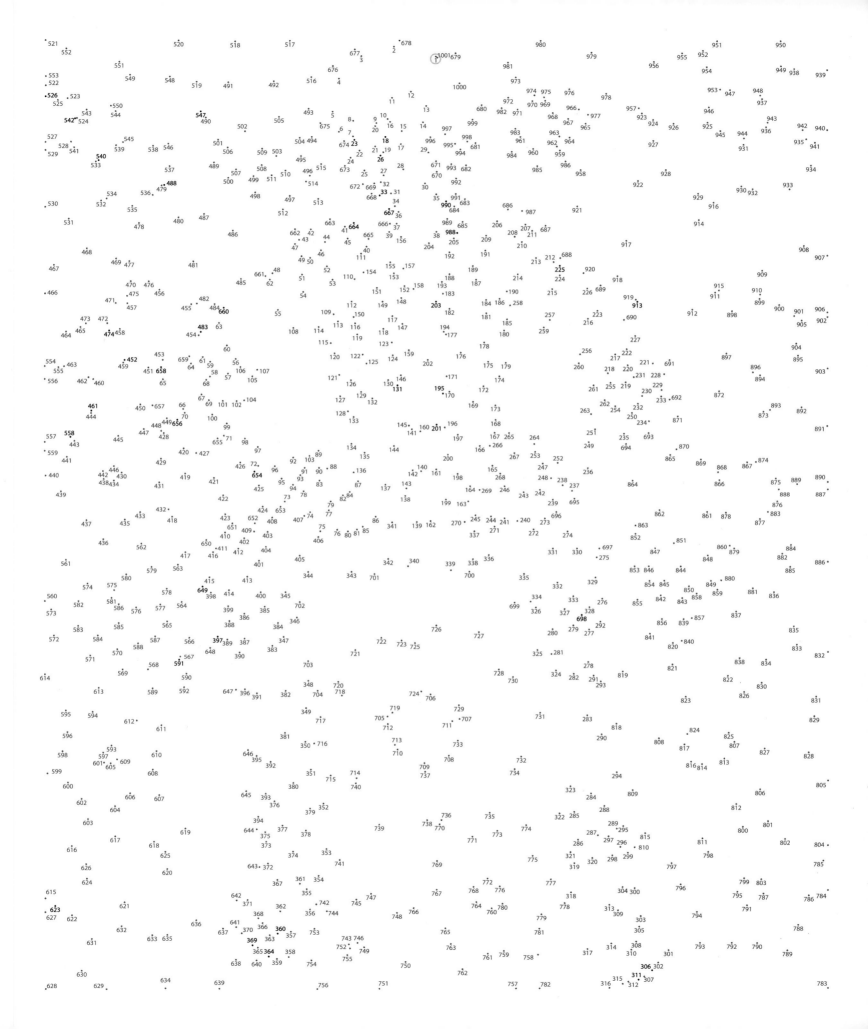

17.

Pan de muerto is not just for the dead. It's a treat for the living too – to the extent that in some regions bakers sell it for months before the day. Of course, there's nothing to stop you from making your own at any time.

18.

Marigolds are placed all over the altar. Fresh, dried, paper or silk – the more, the better. The same goes for the *calaveras*. These are human skulls, usually made of sugar, though not necessarily meant to be eaten.

19.

Calaveras have been made since the seventeenth century, and the traditional methods are time-consuming. Their creators may take up to six months preparing for the season, and the designs may include beads, feathers and even sequins.

20.

If you want to decorate your own sugar skulls, you'll need icing – lots of it, and in as many colours as possible. And you'll also need plenty of time. Not just for the decorations but also for the icing to dry.

21.

There are, of course, skulls for eating. Some are made
from sugar, often flavoured with vanilla; others are made
from chocolate. And if a skull makes you squeamish,
try a coffin instead. Or a skeleton. Or a cross.

22.

It was the Spanish who introduced sugar, after realizing that they had conquered an area perfect for its production. They also introduced the European tradition of making religious decorations from sugar – which was now plentiful, and cheap.

23.

At the Feria del Alfeñique, which takes place every year in Toluca, the makers of sugar skulls compete for awards. From mid-October to the beginning of November, they sell their wares under the arches of Los Portales.

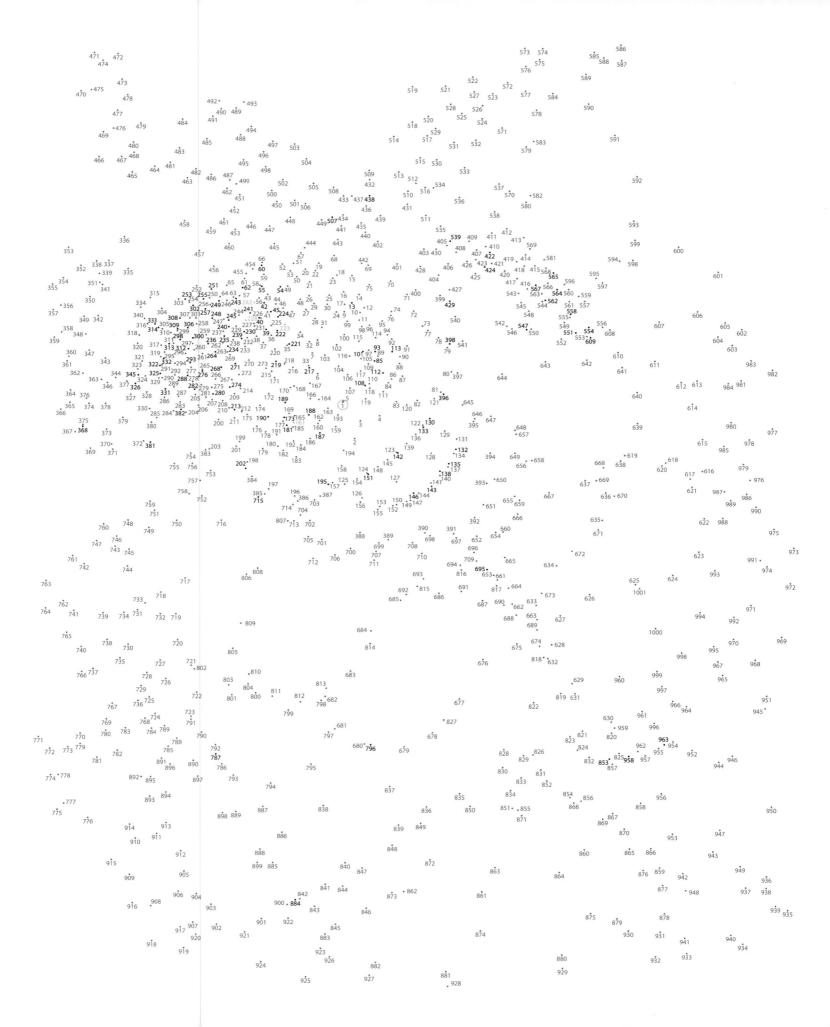

24.

A skull placed on an altar traditionally carries the names
of the dead on its forehead. A small skull is for a dead child,
a full-size skull for adults. Once the altar has been taken
down, these skulls are often thrown away.

25.

It is traditional to burn copal on the altar. Copal is a tree resin, burnt at ceremonies for thousands of years by both Aztecs and Mayans. Its purpose is to bring together heaven and earth.

26.

Día de los Muertos actually refers only to the final day,
2 November. The previous day is dedicated to children
and is known as *El Día de los Angelitos* (little angels).
It recalls the Aztec Little Feast for the Dead.

27.

The *angelitos* are said to return to their families at midnight on 31 October. In some regions, the family will wait at the cemetery all night to welcome the children the moment they return to earth.

28.

This is not a time of mourning. Rather, it is a time to celebrate the links between the living and the dead. Indeed, families believe that their *angelitos* will now intercede for them with God.

29.

Adult souls return on 2 November, and this is the day when families visit the cemetery. Here the village band may be playing while tombs are cleaned and decorated, and families may then share a picnic.

30.

The day has come to be associated with Catrina. An elegantly dressed skeleton, she was originally meant to satirize those Mexicans, particularly aristocrats, who denied their heritages and preferred to pass as Europeans.

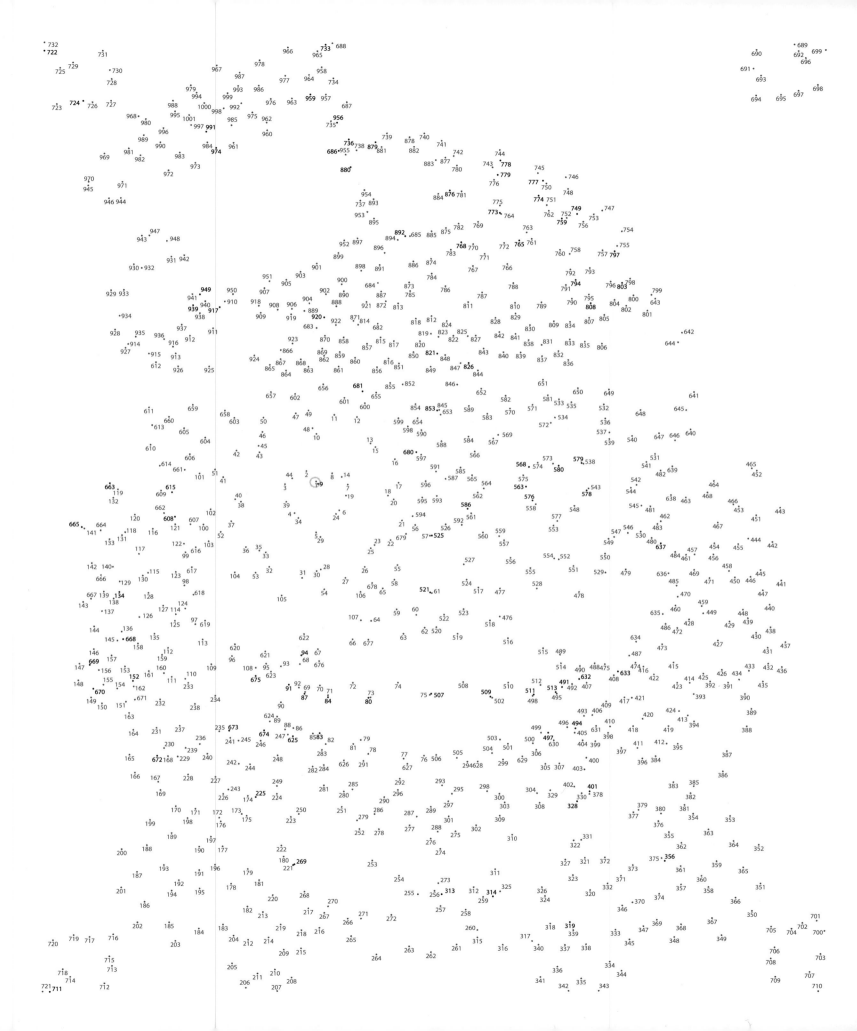

31.

Catrina was the creation of José Guadalupe Posada, a Mexican illustrator protesting against the conditions that would lead to the Mexican Revolution. As the rich took control of the land, *campesinos* (peasant farmers) struggled to make a living.

32.

Posada's image is a skull wearing an extravagantly decorated hat. Later, the artist Diego Rivera painted her full-length, in a mural where she stands centre-stage. Strolling through a park, she is surrounded by notable figures from Mexican history.

33.

The mural, titled *Dream of a Sunday Afternoon in the Alamada Central,* has a darker side, though. Catrina seems not to notice the police officer confronting an indigenous family, or the horse trampling a man as he is shot in the face.

34.

It may also be Rivera who gave Catrina her name. In Spanish, *catrin* means both "well dressed" and "honoured". The original satirical intent is clear. Today she is the mistress of ceremonies, the woman everyone wants to be.

35.

In her finery, Catrina serves as a reminder that death comes to us all – and breaks down the barriers between rich and poor. She also looks ridiculous. We respect death but we can also make jokes.

36.

Expect to see multiple Catrinas at parades and street parties, accompanied by multiple bridegrooms. For the parade in Mexico City, an event involving the whole community, people will have worked for months creating the elaborate costumes.

37.
In some regions, 1 November is the day for costume.
Participants dress in character – priests, devils, widows –
and form a funeral procession that goes from house to house,
dancing and praying. A brass band accompanies them.

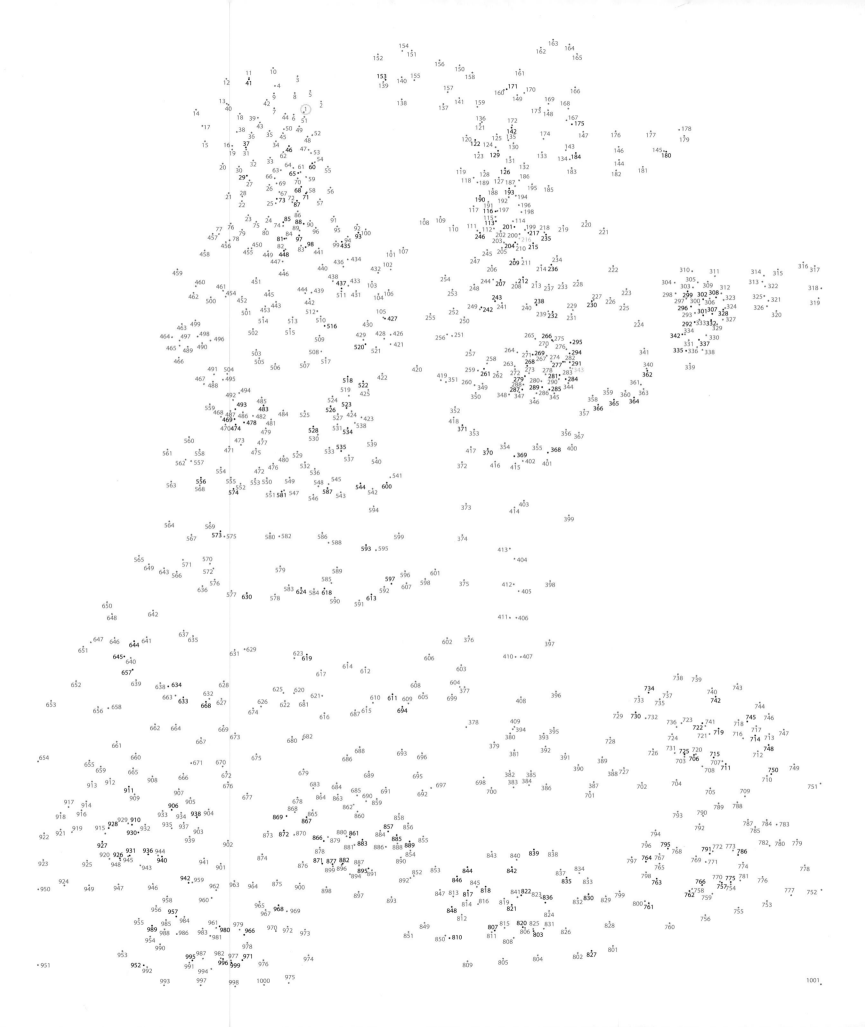

38.

The spectacle in Mexico City attracts millions from around
the world. No wonder it caught the eye of the producers
of the James Bond films. To film their own parade at
the start of *Spectre*, they made ten giant skeletons and
a quarter of a million paper flowers.

39.

The Day of the Dead has only recently become a national holiday in Mexico. The purpose was political: to bring people together via their traditions – even if these were relatively new in some parts of the country where other influences were stronger.

40.

The north of Mexico was a region where the Aztec influence was weak, and the Catholic Church's was strong. Rejecting what they regarded as pagan rituals, the people there preferred to celebrate All Souls' Day.

41.

Today, the Day of the Dead is also celebrated in the
United States. It has travelled wherever Mexicans have
settled: Texas, Arizona and California, in particular.
The day is often an inclusive celebration of Mexican culture.

42.

UNESCO, which aims to protect the world's cultural heritage, put the Day of the Dead on its list of Intangible Cultural Heritage in 2008. By recognising the value of customs, it hopes to highlight the importance of cultural diversity.

1

2

3

4

5

6

7

8

9

10

11

12

13

14

15

16

17

18

19

20

21

22

23

24

25

26

27

28

29

30

31

32

33

34

35

36

37

38

39

40

41

42

THIS IS A CARLTON BOOK

Published by Carlton Books Ltd
20 Mortimer Street
London W1T 3JW

Copyright © 2016 Carlton Books Ltd

A CIP catalogue record for this book is available from the British Library

2 4 6 8 10 9 7 5 3 1

ISBN 978-1-78097-888-8

Printed in China

All dot to dot puzzles created by Patricia Moffett

All images supplied by iStockphoto & Shutterstock.com with the exception
of the following: Getty Images 5, 7, 11, 33, 86, 86, 87, 89

With special thanks to Jason Ward